THE LAND THAT TIME FORGOT

Edgar Rice Burroughs

CAMPFIRE™

KALYANI NAVYUG MEDIA PVT LTD

New Delhi

Sitting around the Campfire, telling the story, were:

Wordsmith	:	Scott Alexander Young
Illustrator	:	KL Jones
Colourist	:	Vikash Gurung
Colour Consultant	:	RC Prakash
Letterer	:	Vishal Sharma
Editors	:	Eman Chowdhary
		Andrew Dodd

Cover Artists:

Illustrator	:	KL Jones
Colourist	:	RC Prakash
Designer	:	Manishi Varshney

Published by Kalyani Navyug Media Pvt Ltd
101 C, Shiv House, Hari Nagar Ashram
New Delhi 110014
India
www.campfire.co.in

ISBN: 978-81-906963-2-6

Printed in india at Rave India

About The Author

Edgar Rice Burroughs was born in Chicago in 1875. He took inspiration for many of his stories from the classical mythology and literature he studied in his youth, and from the time he spent at an Idaho ranch set up by his brothers. There he rode the range, herded cattle, and befriended characters that were straight out of the wild west. His parents were alarmed at some of the new friends he had made, and sent him to the Michigan Military Academy, from where he graduated in 1895. Unsure of what to do with his life, and rejected by West Point Military Academy, he joined the army as a private. He hoped to become an officer, and did not have to wait long. As he was a natural horseman, he was transferred to the famous Seventh Cavalry.

After being discharged from the army due to a medical problem, he returned to civilian life. In 1900, he married his childhood sweetheart, Emma Centennia Hulbert. Following this, he tried his hand at various odd jobs, including being a railway policeman and a door-to-door salesman. By 1911, he was penniless, with a wife and two children to support. Things were not looking particularly good.

His life then took a turn for the better. The story goes that, while proofreading an advertisement for pencil sharpeners in a pulp magazine, inspiration struck. Looking through various magazines, with their tall tales of adventure, he was motivated to write a fantasy story himself. *A Princess of Mars* appeared as a novel in 1912, and his career as a professional writer took off. Another phenomenally successful novel was *Tarzan of the Apes*, published in 1914. The character Tarzan went on to become a legend in his own right.

In 1934, Edgar Rice Burroughs divorced his wife, Emma, and married Florence Dearholt the following year. In 1940, with the war raging in Europe, the couple moved to Hawaii, but this marriage also ended in divorce. Burroughs was too old to be called to active service in World War II. Instead, at the age of 66, he became the oldest war correspondent to serve in the Pacific. He died on 19th March 1950, having written well over 50 novels.

Bowen

Lys

Olson

Nobs

Baron Von
Schoenvorts

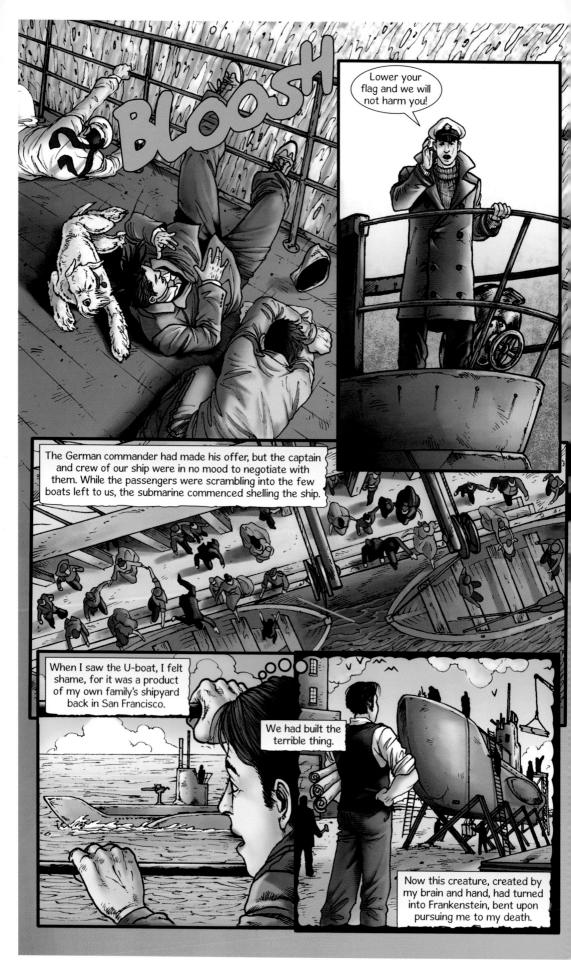

BLOOSH

Lower your flag and we will not harm you!

The German commander had made his offer, but the captain and crew of our ship were in no mood to negotiate with them. While the passengers were scrambling into the few boats left to us, the submarine commenced shelling the ship.

When I saw the U-boat, I felt shame, for it was a product of my own family's shipyard back in San Francisco.

We had built the terrible thing.

Now this creature, created by my brain and hand, had turned into Frankenstein, bent upon pursuing me to my death.

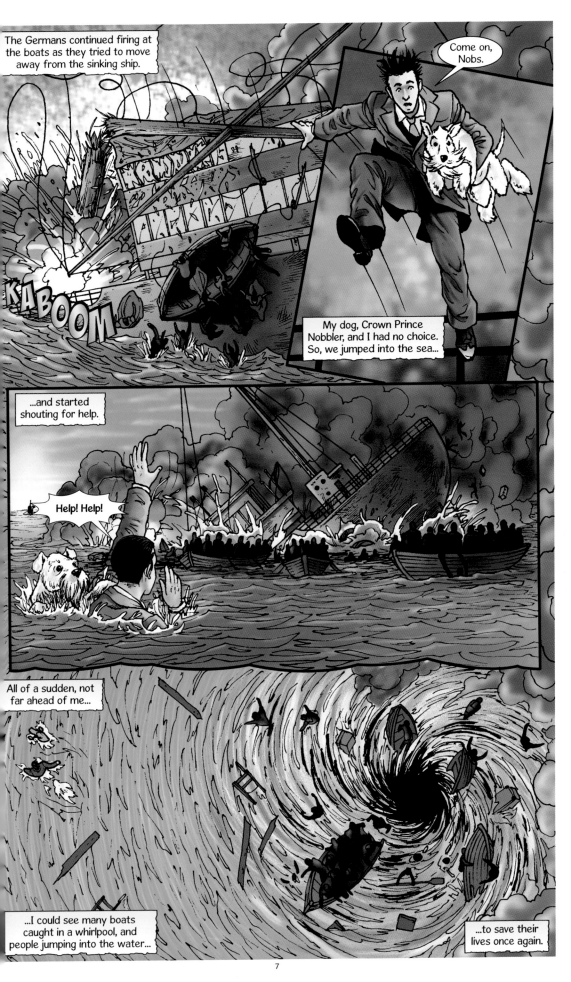

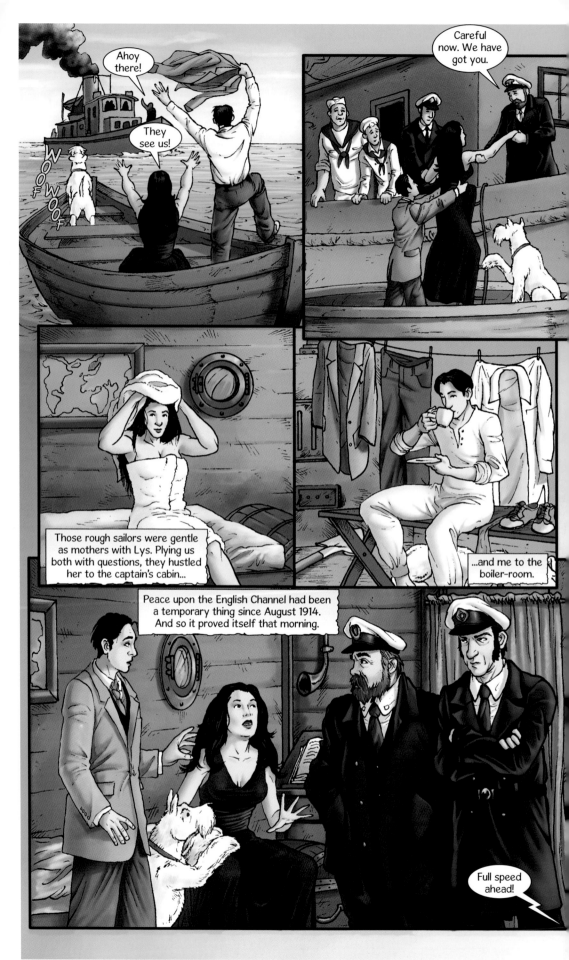

Not a bad day's work, but we lost the captain. Does anyone know anything about running a submarine?

No. How are you going to run her? You cannot trust these men.

You are right. I do not know anytime about a sub.

But I do!

I know more about this particular sub than the officer who commanded her.

We were still planning our next move, when the captain of the U-boat came towards us.

And I am sure this U-boat's crew will help us. Then they can spend the rest of the war in a nice, warm POW camp.

Lys seemed to go pale on seeing him.

If they help you, they are traitors.

She told me later that the captain of the U-boat was the German she was to marry. He was Baron Von Schoenvorts.

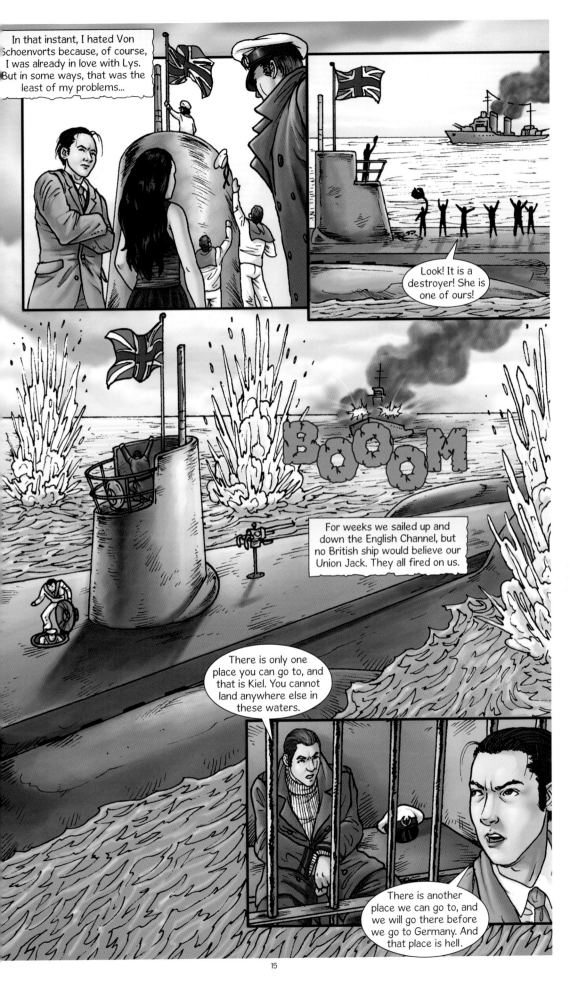

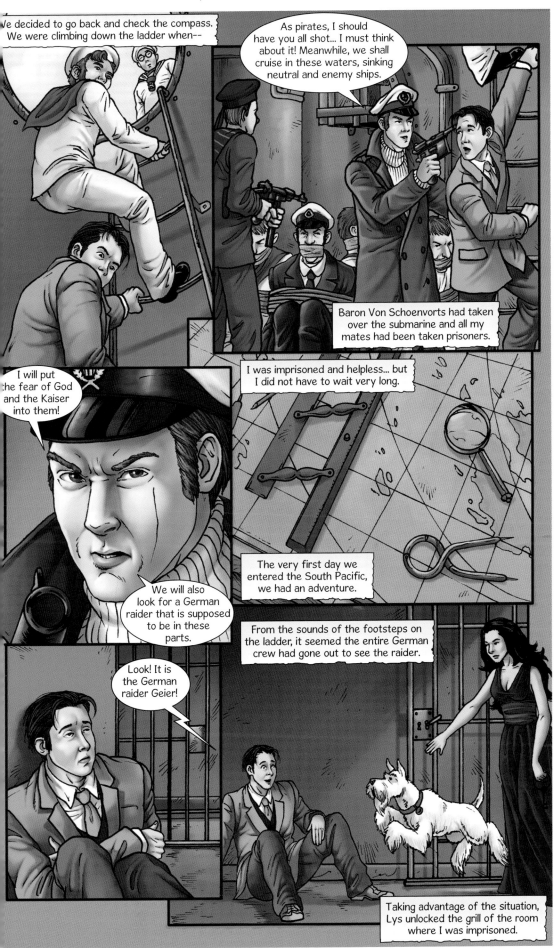

We decided to go back and check the compass. We were climbing down the ladder when--

As pirates, I should have you all shot... I must think about it! Meanwhile, we shall cruise in these waters, sinking neutral and enemy ships.

Baron Von Schoenvorts had taken over the submarine and all my mates had been taken prisoners.

I will put the fear of God and the Kaiser into them!

I was imprisoned and helpless... but I did not have to wait very long.

The very first day we entered the South Pacific, we had an adventure.

We will also look for a German raider that is supposed to be in these parts.

From the sounds of the footsteps on the ladder, it seemed the entire German crew had gone out to see the raider.

Look! It is the German raider Geier!

Taking advantage of the situation, Lys unlocked the grill of the room where I was imprisoned.

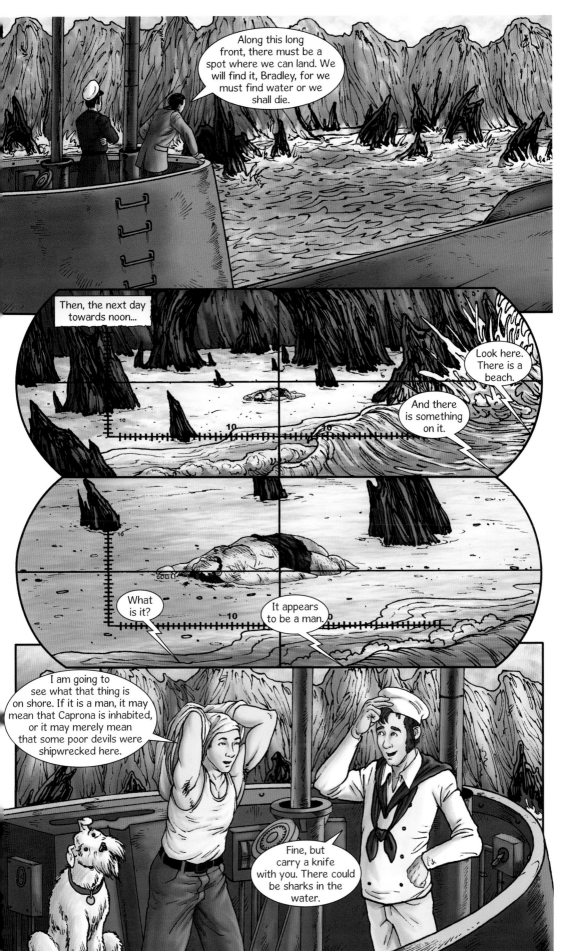

Nobs proved to be a faithful dog once again. He jumped in the water after me.

Come on, Nobs.

The tide was not strong, and there was no undertow, so we made it to shore easily.

I walked towards the creature.

Whatever it was, it had been dead for some time.

I could not say whether it was an ape or a man, for it resembled neither.

GRRRRWWLLL

26

It is the underground channel of an inland river. I am sure there are fertile lands and fresh water beyond those cliffs!

Yes, sir, behind the cliffs! You spoke a true word, sir – behind the cliffs!

To the diving stations.

At that moment, I felt a foreboding of evil, but I did not say anything to the others.

Where were we going? What lay at the end of this great sewer?

Had we said farewell to sunlight and life forever, or were there even greater dangers ahead of us than those which we faced now?

I did not know what lay in store for us.

I thought I saw wide, swollen jaws, and then all was blotted out.

A shiver ran down into the tower as the thing closed upon the periscope. A moment later, it was gone, and I could see again.

Above the trees I could see a huge thing with wings – a creature as large as a whale, but fashioned more like a lizard.

Then again something charged at the periscope and blotted out the mirror. I was almost gasping for breath as I gave the commands to emerge.

The flora and fauna around us was so strange that it seemed unreal.

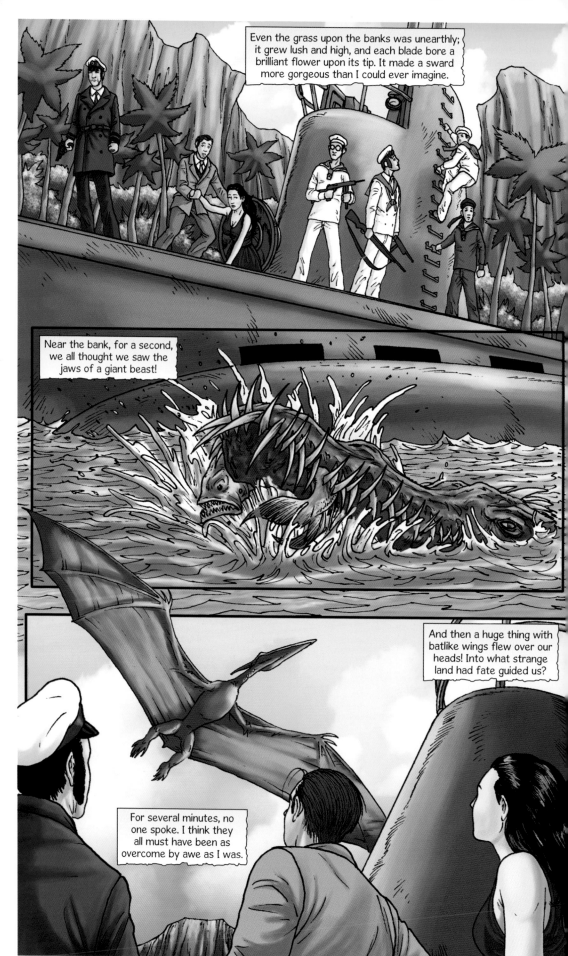

Even the grass upon the banks was unearthly; it grew lush and high, and each blade bore a brilliant flower upon its tip. It made a sward more gorgeous than I could ever imagine.

Near the bank, for a second, we all thought we saw the jaws of a giant beast!

And then a huge thing with batlike wings flew over our heads! Into what strange land had fate guided us?

For several minutes, no one spoke. I think they all must have been as overcome by awe as I was.

This strange place swarmed with life.

We could see huge creatures moving upon the ground in the thick forest...

..while the bosom of the river wriggled with living things.

We saw creatures that we are taught have been extinct for millions of years.

Look! Take a look at the giraffe coming out of the river?

What is that thing?

Look out. It is coming at you!

Aiiieeeee

The thing must have been sixteen or eighteen feet in length, and closely resembled pictures I had seen of plesiosaurs from the Jurassic era.

Lys looked disgusted at the thought.

And besides, Mr Olson was just saying that to get all the steaks for himself.

Do not worry, Miss La Rue. It cannot be the same reptile. That was nearly forty miles down river.

That is right, miss.

If the whole land is infested by these horrid monsters--

Then life would be impossible upon it!

But we must search for fresh water, and for meat and fruits. We should go back.

Yes.

We did not see the creatures while we were getting under way, though I had the cannon raised to the deck and manned against an assault.

The trees were full of monkeys of all sizes. Once, we thought we saw a manlike creature watching from the trees.

That sounds fair. We are ready to work with you.

It was understood that we were to act as a military organisation guided by military rules and discipline. I was the commander, with Bradley as my first lieutenant and Olson as my second, in command of the Englishmen.

Von Schoenvorts was to act as an additional second lieutenant and have charge of his own men.

The four of us were to constitute a military court under which men could be tried and sentenced to punishment for breaking rules and discipline.

Once the rules were laid out, we set off to work.

Alright, old man, you can come too.

We took a party, consisting of both Germans and English, and went hunting.

43

Nobs, old boy!

Thankfully, Nobs was unharmed except for minor bruises.

I was busy patting Nobs when--

My god!

What Von Schoenvorts had spotted was a collection of nearly five hundred creatures. It was hard to say whether they were ape or man.

Some of them resembled the corpse we had found on the beach, while others were of a lower type, looking more like the apes. And some were uncannily manlike – standing erect, being less hairy and possessing better-shaped heads.

We decided to take him with us, and by means of belts, we managed to place a leash around his neck.

We felt that we had taught these creatures a lesson because of which we would be safer in the future – at least, safer from them.

The next morning, we began building a base camp. Anything had to be better than more time confined within that submarine. We called it Fort Dinosaur.

Bradley, Olson, Von Schoenvorts, Miss La Rue, and I sat up half the night drawing plans.

The men were set to work felling trees. Half the men laboured while the other half stood guard, alternating each hour, with an hour off at noon. Olson directed this work.

Bradley, Von Schoenvorts and I, with Miss La Rue's help, staked out the huts and the outer wall.

Then the building operations started.

But Von Schoenvorts did not help with manual labour. He was too proud to do that.

The next day, when some of the men were chopping wood, one of them threw away a small branch, which unfortunately struck Von Schoenvorts. It could not have hurt him, for it did not leave a mark...

...but he flew into a terrific rage.

Attention! Pig!

It was too much for me to bear--

Think again, Von Schoenvorts!

Von Schoenvorts sulked downstairs that night, while the rest of us watched the sunset in Caprona.

Atis! Atis!

Our journey was adventurous. We saw a strange creature which Ahm called Atis. We saw many apes on the way back, and one of the men swore he saw a man among them.

Bradley had many stories for us when he returned.

We suffered no casualties and there was no illness. We must go on another expedition.

Agreed. We must.

living upon meat. A of the and

8th October 1916: Much has happened since I last wrote. Bradley is away again on another expedition to the cliffs. Ahm has disappeared. He has been gone about three days; but the most startling thing I have on record is that while out hunting the other day, Von Schoenvorts and Olson...

...discovered a geyser of oil! I went with Olson, Von Schoenvorts and Lys to see this geyser for myself.

If we succeed in refining this oil, we can leave Caprona and return to our own world.

So we helped Von Schoenvorts build his primitive refinery. We worked with him for two days until he got things going...

...and then we returned to Fort Dinosaur, as I feared Bradley might return and be worried by our absence.

On our way back, I decided to tell Lys what I felt for her.

I love you, Lys.

I love you too.

That was the happiest night of my life...

...but the next morning was one of the worst.

52

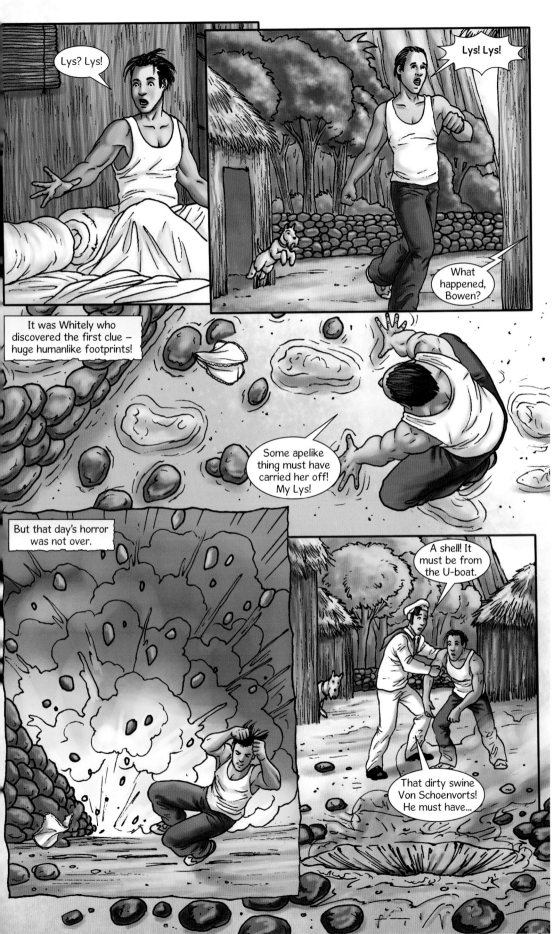

...he must have succeeded in refining the oil. Now we will never get out of this godforsaken place!

When we returned to the fort, we speculated whether an ape-man or Von Schoenvorts had abducted Lys. From what we knew of him, he seemed capable of doing such a thing. But those giant footprints?

I decided to follow them, and see if I could rescue Lys.

After I had travelled some distance, I found a piece of muslin. It had to be a sign left by Lys that she had been carried that way. As I went on, I found more bits of muslin. I knew Lys still lived.

I followed the trail and travelled over twenty miles that day. I had been hardened to hiking by the hunting.

As I approached some lofty cliffs, I could smell the pungent aroma of woodsmoke. Looking over, I saw--

Lys!

She was a captive of this tribe, the Hatchet men I called them. They seemed more advanced than Ahm, though the language they spoke was similar. So similar, I could work out the gist of it.

I am Tsa. This is my she. Who wishes her more than Tsa?

I answered in Ahm's language.

I do.

Who are you? I kill! I kill! I kill!

The she is mine, and I have come to claim her. I kill if you do not let her come to me.

Finally, after reminding him what my rifle was capable of doing, he allowed us to stay in Tsa's cave.

In spite of everything we had been through, and the beasts outside the cave, we fell asleep. We were exhausted.

The next morning we had company, when the Hatchet men gathered outside our cave. They were friendlier this time.

Do any of you know Ahm? Ahm?

Back there we may have known him.

You came from back there?

We all come from back there. After a while we go there. Become Galus.

After breakfast, the men set out to hunt, while the women went to a large pool of warm water covered with green scum and filled with billions of tadpoles. They waded in about a foot deep and lay down in the mud.

Why do you do that?

Ata. Ata.

I had given my pistol to Lys, but she never had to use it, for no reptile or beast ever approached the pool while the women were there.

57

Meanwhile, I went hunting with some of the Hatchet men. They were content to feed on the smaller beasts, but I went in search of deer.

And then somewhere along the way, I became hopelessly lost.

While finding my way back, I came across a gravestone. It was a discovery that filled me at first with hope...

...and then despair.

HERE LIES JOHN TIPPET, ENGLISHMAN CILLED BY TYRANNOSAURUS 10 SEPT., A.D. 1916 R. I. P.

Tippet had accompanied Bradley in his expedition.

Tippet's grave was evidence that Bradley had gone that far upon his expedition, and that he was probably lost too. I was so grief-stricken that I did not realise I was being watched by cavemen!

Suddenly, I felt a warm hand on me...

In that moment, I was glad of the jujutsu training I had done for several years back in California.

It took me just about thirty seconds to break the elbow of one of my assailants, trip another and send him stumbling backwards among his fellows...

...and throw the third completely over my head in such a way that when he fell his neck was broken.

The other members of the party stood in mute and inactive surprise, so I unslung my rifle, and aimed at them. I could tell they would charge.

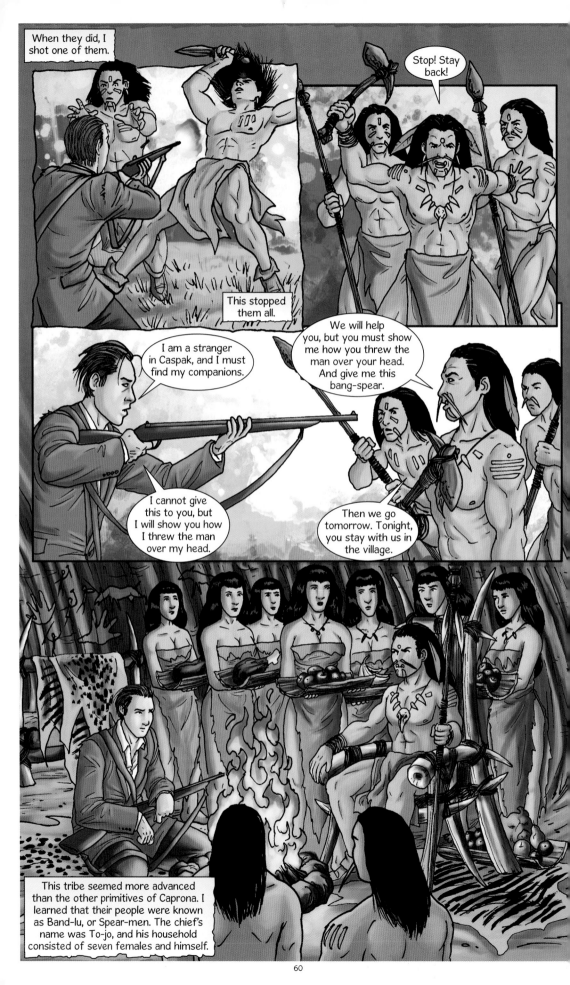

One of them, So-ta, was almost pretty. After all my years of shyness, I was becoming a ladies' man until...

...she took such a lively interest in me that To-jo objected to her attentions.

Stop! What are you doing? That is no way to treat a lady!

You must not hit her again.

Later that night, So-ta confided in me.

Soon I must leave. So-ta soon to be Kro-lu.

Kro-lu? Yet another tribe?

I fell asleep, lost in dreams full of wild theories about human evolution in this strange land.

After days of walking, I reached the cliffs of another tribe. It looked like there had been a massacre. My only glimmer of hope was that there was not one homo sapien skull. Not one that could have belonged to Lys anyway.

I walked fruther till I came across another gravestone. Never in my life had I felt more hopeless or helpless. I was lost. I could not find my friends.

But somehow, I kept going.

WILLIAM JAMES, 13TH SEPTEMBER 1916. KILLED BY SABRE-TOOTHED TIGER.

For days and weeks, I searched for Lys and for the Hatchet men of Caprona, amidst all the horrors and dangers of the ancient world.

All the fears and sorrows of the past were wiped away, and once again, I was the happiest of men.

But what has happened to you in these last months? I almost fear to ask.

Since then, Kho has pursued me, and I have fled by night and by day to avoid him.'

For several weeks, I lived as a cave-girl with the tribe of Hatchet men. Then they were driven from their caves by another tribe which had slain many and carried off half the females.

'For a time, Nobs was all the protection I required, but one day he disappeared. I have not seen him since. Fate was kinder to us, Bowen.'

CAMPFIRE™

About Us

It is night-time in the forest. The sky is black, studded with countless stars. A campfire is crackling, and the storytelling has begun. Stories about love and wisdom, conflict and power, dreams and identity, courage and adventure, survival against all odds, and hope against all hope – they have all come to the fore in a stream of words, gestures, song and dance. The warm, cheerful radiance of the campfire has awoken the storyteller in all those present. Even the trees and the earth and the animals of the forest seem to have fallen silent, captivated, bewitched.

Inspired by this enduring relationship between a campfire and the stories it evokes, we began publishing under the Campfire imprint in 2008, with the vision of creating graphic novels of the finest quality to entertain and educate our readers. Our writers, editors, artists and colourists share a deep passion for good stories and the art of storytelling, so our books are well researched, beautifully illustrated and wonderfully written to create a most enjoyable reading experience.

Our graphic novels are presently being published in four exciting categories. The *Classics* category showcases popular and timeless literature, which has been faithfully adapted for today's readers. While these adaptations retain the flavour of the era, they encourage our readers to delve into the literary world with the aid of authentic graphics and simplified language. Titles in the *Originals* category feature imaginative new characters and intriguing plots, and will be highly anticipated and appreciated by lovers of fiction. Our *Mythology* titles tap into the vast library of epics, myths, and legends from India and abroad, not just presenting tales from time immemorial, but also addressing their modern-day relevance. And our *Biography* titles explore the life and times of eminent personalities from around the world, in a manner that is both inspirational and personal.

Crafted by a new generation of talented artists and writers, all our graphic novels boast cutting-edge artwork, an engaging narrative, and have universal and lasting appeal.

Whether you are an avid reader or an occasional one, we hope you will gather around our campfire and let us draw you into our fascinating world of storytelling.

What is a Tugboat?

A tugboat, or tug, is a boat with powerful engines that can push or pull very large ships.

Tugs help to move ships into position or drag them out into sea. They can also rescue ships which need repairs, and tow them back to port. Some tugboats can act as fire engines too. They contain powerful pumps, which take water from the sea, and use it to extinguish fires on oil rigs, ships, and structures on shore. Tugboats can be 70 to 210 feet (21-64 metres) long, and their engines can generate between 750 and 3,000 horsepower. Tugboats originally contained steam engines, but today diesel engines are more commonly used. Improvements to the tugboat design continue to be developed.

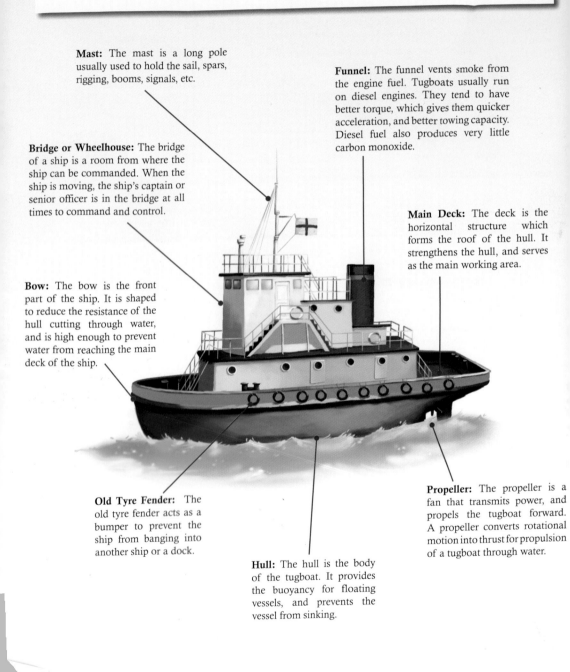

Mast: The mast is a long pole usually used to hold the sail, spars, rigging, booms, signals, etc.

Funnel: The funnel vents smoke from the engine fuel. Tugboats usually run on diesel engines. They tend to have better torque, which gives them quicker acceleration, and better towing capacity. Diesel fuel also produces very little carbon monoxide.

Bridge or Wheelhouse: The bridge of a ship is a room from where the ship can be commanded. When the ship is moving, the ship's captain or senior officer is in the bridge at all times to command and control.

Main Deck: The deck is the horizontal structure which forms the roof of the hull. It strengthens the hull, and serves as the main working area.

Bow: The bow is the front part of the ship. It is shaped to reduce the resistance of the hull cutting through water, and is high enough to prevent water from reaching the main deck of the ship.

Old Tyre Fender: The old tyre fender acts as a bumper to prevent the ship from banging into another ship or a dock.

Propeller: The propeller is a fan that transmits power, and propels the tugboat forward. A propeller converts rotational motion into thrust for propulsion of a tugboat through water.

Hull: The hull is the body of the tugboat. It provides the buoyancy for floating vessels, and prevents the vessel from sinking.

CAMPFIRE™

About Us

It is night-time in the forest. The sky is black, studded with countless stars. A campfire is crackling, and the storytelling has begun. Stories about love and wisdom, conflict and power, dreams and identity, courage and adventure, survival against all odds, and hope against all hope – they have all come to the fore in a stream of words, gestures, song and dance. The warm, cheerful radiance of the campfire has awoken the storyteller in all those present. Even the trees and the earth and the animals of the forest seem to have fallen silent, captivated, bewitched.

Inspired by this enduring relationship between a campfire and the stories it evokes, we began publishing under the Campfire imprint in 2008, with the vision of creating graphic novels of the finest quality to entertain and educate our readers. Our writers, editors, artists and colourists share a deep passion for good stories and the art of storytelling, so our books are well researched, beautifully illustrated and wonderfully written to create a most enjoyable reading experience.

Our graphic novels are presently being published in four exciting categories. The *Classics* category showcases popular and timeless literature, which has been faithfully adapted for today's readers. While these adaptations retain the flavour of the era, they encourage our readers to delve into the literary world with the aid of authentic graphics and simplified language. Titles in the *Originals* category feature imaginative new characters and intriguing plots, and will be highly anticipated and appreciated by lovers of fiction. Our *Mythology* titles tap into the vast library of epics, myths, and legends from India and abroad, not just presenting tales from time immemorial, but also addressing their modern-day relevance. And our *Biography* titles explore the life and times of eminent personalities from around the world, in a manner that is both inspirational and personal.

Crafted by a new generation of talented artists and writers, all our graphic novels boast cutting-edge artwork, an engaging narrative, and have universal and lasting appeal.

Whether you are an avid reader or an occasional one, we hope you will gather around our campfire and let us draw you into our fascinating world of storytelling.

What is a Tugboat?

A tugboat, or tug, is a boat with powerful engines that can push or pull very large ships.

Tugs help to move ships into position or drag them out into sea. They can also rescue ships which need repairs, and tow them back to port. Some tugboats can act as fire engines too. They contain powerful pumps, which take water from the sea, and use it to extinguish fires on oil rigs, ships, and structures on shore. Tugboats can be 70 to 210 feet (21-64 metres) long, and their engines can generate between 750 and 3,000 horsepower. Tugboats originally contained steam engines, but today diesel engines are more commonly used. Improvements to the tugboat design continue to be developed.

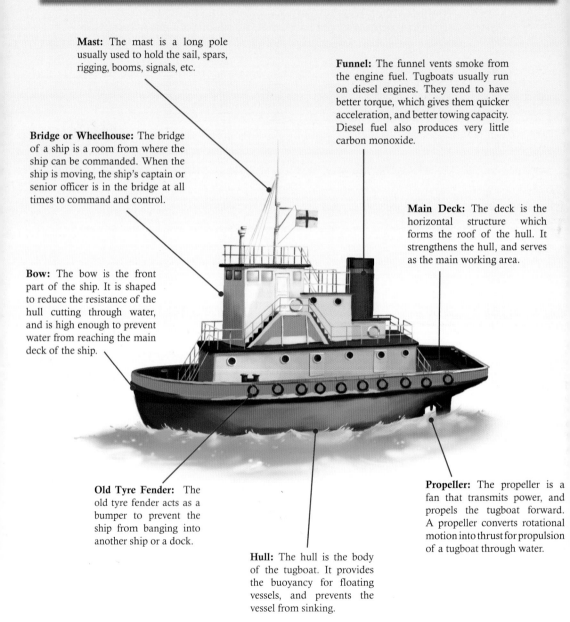

Mast: The mast is a long pole usually used to hold the sail, spars, rigging, booms, signals, etc.

Funnel: The funnel vents smoke from the engine fuel. Tugboats usually run on diesel engines. They tend to have better torque, which gives them quicker acceleration, and better towing capacity. Diesel fuel also produces very little carbon monoxide.

Bridge or Wheelhouse: The bridge of a ship is a room from where the ship can be commanded. When the ship is moving, the ship's captain or senior officer is in the bridge at all times to command and control.

Main Deck: The deck is the horizontal structure which forms the roof of the hull. It strengthens the hull, and serves as the main working area.

Bow: The bow is the front part of the ship. It is shaped to reduce the resistance of the hull cutting through water, and is high enough to prevent water from reaching the main deck of the ship.

Old Tyre Fender: The old tyre fender acts as a bumper to prevent the ship from banging into another ship or a dock.

Propeller: The propeller is a fan that transmits power, and propels the tugboat forward. A propeller converts rotational motion into thrust for propulsion of a tugboat through water.

Hull: The hull is the body of the tugboat. It provides the buoyancy for floating vessels, and prevents the vessel from sinking.

What is a Submarine?

A submarine is a vessel that can be submerged and navigated under water, usually built for warfare, and armed with torpedoes or guided missiles.

Submarines have always been a popular source for fiction writers in books such as *20,000 Leagues Under the Sea* and *The Hunt for Red October*. The *Turtle* is the earliest-known submarine, and was built in 1776. It had a crude and primitive design which resembled a wooden barrel. It contained a set of pedals which were used to operate its propellers. Submarines became more developed over time, and production was later increased due to World War I. One of the most well-known submarines of that time was the German U-boat (short for underwater boat). In the world wars, the U-boats sank thousands of vessels which they attacked, using deadly torpedoes. They would also lay mines around the English coast to try and sabotage English ships. In modern times, submarines have become ever more deadly. The British Trafalgar-class submarine carries American-made Tomahawk cruise missiles, which have a range of a 1,000 miles.

Tail Plane: The tail plane consists of:-
a. Diving Plane: An adjustable rudder at the stern that allows the submarine to dive and surface.
b. Upper Rudder: A movable part that allows the submarine to stay on course, and turn right and left.

Sail: The sail normally holds the entrance hatch. Usually, the sail, and the very top of the submarine, is visible above the waves.

Periscope: The periscope is the eye of the submarine. It was invented and developed solely for the purpose of providing a means to view the surface without being detected by a surface craft.

Main Ballast Tanks: The ballast tanks take in water when the submarine needs to submerge. The buoyancy of the submarine is dictated by the amount of water taken into the ballast tanks.

Torpedo: A torpedo is a self-propelled, cigar-shaped missile which contains an explosive charge. Often equipped with a homing device, it is launched from a submarine or other warships to destroy surface vessels and other submarines.

Sonar: The sonar helps a submarine detect other objects in the water. It works by sending out a sound wave. When this sound wave strikes an object, a portion of the sound is echoed back to the submarine.

DID YOU KNOW?

The typhoon-class submarines (from Russia) are the largest in the world. They are also extremely quiet vessels. They can stay submerged in water for months, making them important during wartime. They have a unique design that helps to make them easier to operate in spite of their size.

Available now

Putting the fun back into reading!